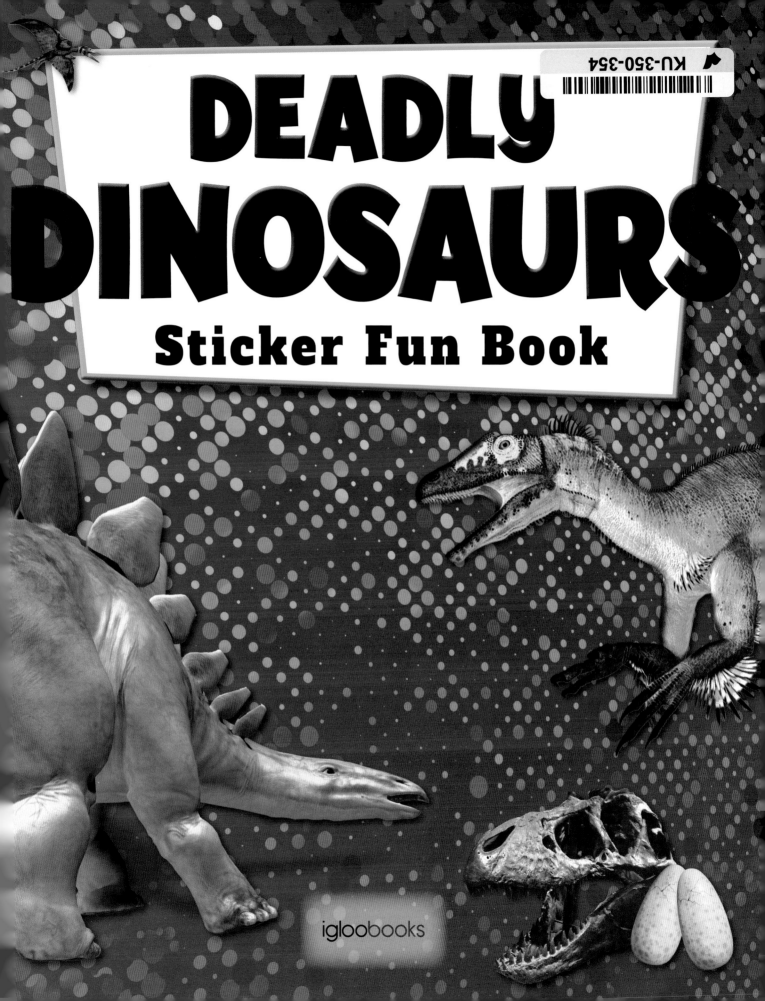

DEADLY DINOSAURS
Sticker Fun Book

igloobooks

Theropods

This carnivorous family of dinosaurs first appeared during the Triassic Period, over 230 million years ago. These dinosaurs were known for being vicious predators and included giants such as Tyrannosaurus rex and Spinosaurus as members. In the Jurassic Period, a branch of Theropods began to evolve separately, leading to the evolution of modern-day birds!

Fact
Carnotaurus had thick ridges of bone above its eyes that looked like scaly eyebrows.

Scary Shadows

The group of dinosaurs called theropods contained some of the scariest creatures in the world. See if you can match up each of these fearsome dinosaurs with their shadows.

Fact
Spinosaurus was the biggest of all the theropods, measuring 6 metres (20 ft) tall!

Carnivore Close-ups

Theropods preyed on other, smaller dinosaurs for food. See if you can match each of these vicious predators with the correct close-up.

2

Answers on page 16

Tyrannosaurus Trails

The Tyrannosaurus rex is sometimes called the king of the dinosaurs. Help the king get to the juicy meat in the centre of the maze by drawing a line through it.

Fact
The reason that it is often called the king of the dinosaurs is because Tyrannosaurus rex translates as 'tyrant lizard king'.

Start

Finish

Fact
All theropods were meat-eaters and had a diet of fish and animals.

Answers on page 18

Marine Reptiles

Though not strictly dinosaurs, marine reptiles were just as huge and scary! These amazing aquatic creatures lived as early as 225 million years ago and some species could reach up to 12 metres (40 feet) long! The largest marine reptiles ate everything under the sea, sometimes even leaping out of the water to catch flying dinosaurs!

Fact
Theories suggest that some prehistoric marine reptiles also spent time living on land!

a b c

d e f

Tri Again

Prehistoric marine reptiles aren't actually considered dinosaurs, but they lived alongside them. See if you can spot the odd one out among these underwater monsters.

Fact
Turtles had prehistoric relatives, too. Archelon, an ancient turtle, lived millions of years ago and was the size of a car!

Hiding Dinosaurs

There are lots of marine reptiles lurking around this dark reef. Count how many of each you can find and write your answers in the boxes below.

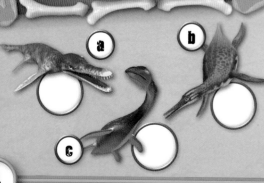

a b

c

4

Answers on page 18

Prehistoric Patterns

Marine reptiles terrorised the seas for millions of years. See if you can spot some of these ancient swimmers in the scene below. Draw a line around each of the sequences.

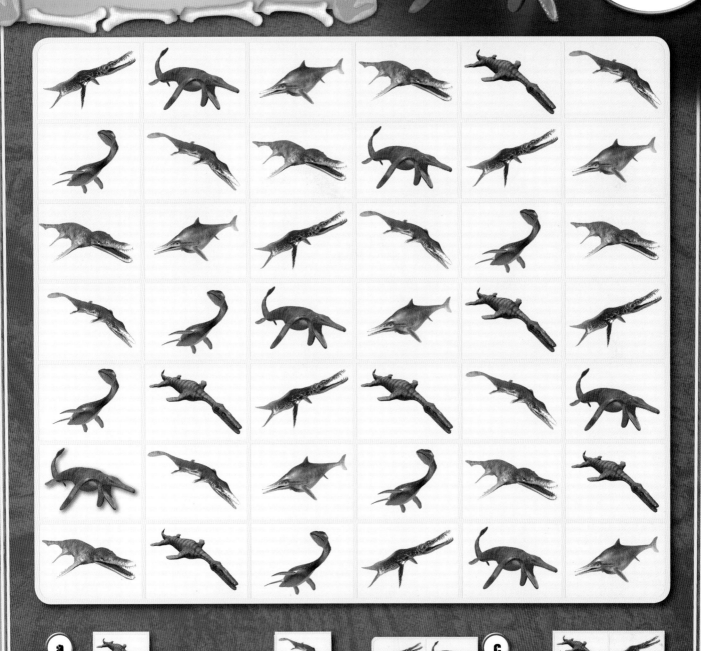

Pterosaurs

The name 'pterosaur' translates as 'winged lizard' and these fearsome flyers terrorised the prehistoric world between 225 and 65 million years ago. They had thin, hollow bones, like modern-day birds, which allowed them to fly. Some, however, were only able to glide, as they didn't have the power to fly on their own.

Fact

Pterosaurs lived through the whole prehistoric era, from the Triassic to the Cretaceous Period, 225 to 65 million years ago.

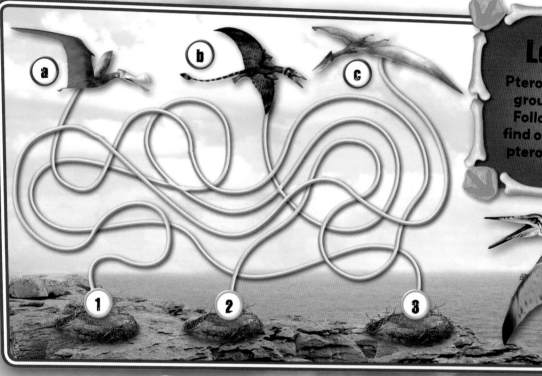

Loop-the-loop

Pterosaurs were the biggest group of flying dinosaurs. Follow each of the lines to find out where each of these pterosaurs has flown from.

Fact

Pterodactylus had a huge finger that spanned from its hand to the tip of its wing.

Matching Hatchlings

Most pterosaurs laid eggs like modern day birds. Can you match each of these fantastic flyers to the nest with the matching pattern of eggs?

6

Dotty Dinosaur

There's a fearsome pterosaur lurking around the jungle. Join the numbered dots together to find out what it is, then decorate the picture with your best pens.

Sauropods

The sauropod family contains the biggest dinosaurs that ever existed. Reaching lengths of up to 35 metres (115 ft) and heights of 18 metres (60 ft) high, they towered over other dinosaurs. They were herbivorous, so they had to eat huge amounts of vegetation to survive. However, they were rarely preyed upon by other animals, as they were just too big to kill!

Fact

At a massive 14 me[...] (46 ft), Mamenchisau[...] had the longest neck [...] all sauropods.

a

b

c

d

Fossil Hunter

Sauropods first appeared in the Triassic Period, around 225 million years ago. Can you work out which of these skeletons belonged to the sauropod Diplodocus?

Diplodocus

Fact

Sauropods took up to sixty years to grow to their full size!

Cretaceous Clues

There were hundreds of different species of sauropods. Use the clues below to match each of the descriptions to the correct sauropod.

a

b

d

Titanosaurus

Titanosaurus was named after the giants of Greek mythology and had pinky-red skin.

Answer........

Saltasaurus

Saltasaurus was a green-skinned sauropod that had rough, stone-like protection on its back.

Answer........

Auchisaurus

Auchisaurus was one of the smaller sauropods, with blue and yellow skin.

Answer........

c

Apatosaurus

This dinosaur, formerly known as Brontosaurus, has grey and brown skin.

Answer........

8

Answers on page 16

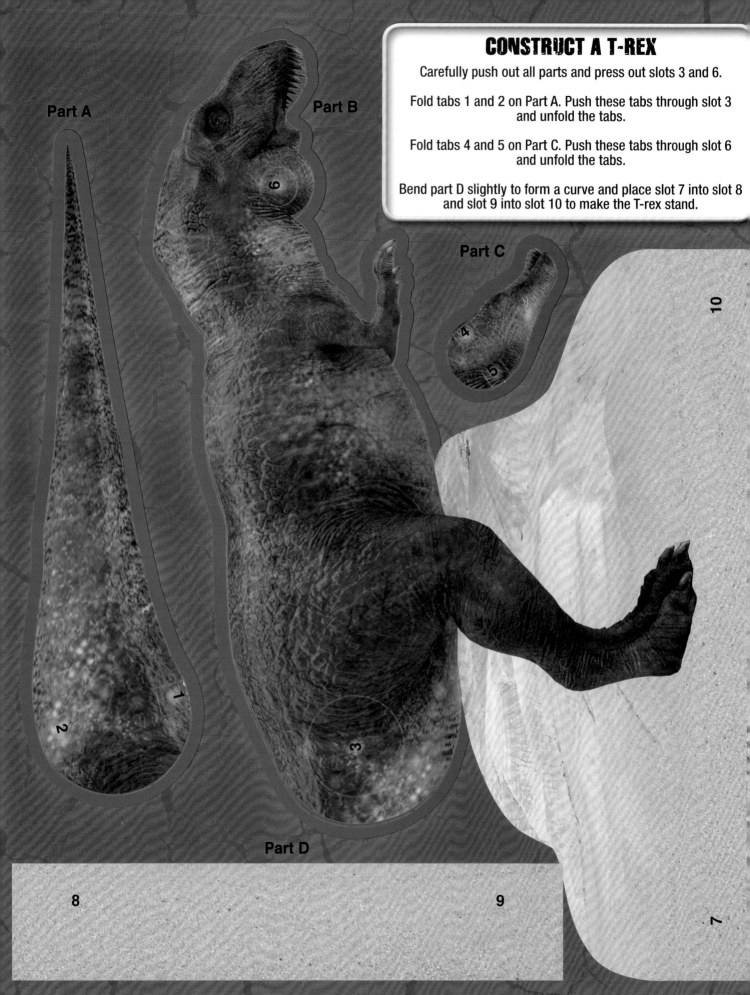

Part A

Part B

Part C

CONSTRUCT A T-REX

Carefully push out all parts and press out slots 3 and 6.

Fold tabs 1 and 2 on Part A. Push these tabs through slot 3 and unfold the tabs.

Fold tabs 4 and 5 on Part C. Push these tabs through slot 6 and unfold the tabs.

Bend part D slightly to form a curve and place slot 7 into slot 8 and slot 9 into slot 10 to make the T-rex stand.

Part D

8

9

Tyrannosaurus Chase - pages 12-13

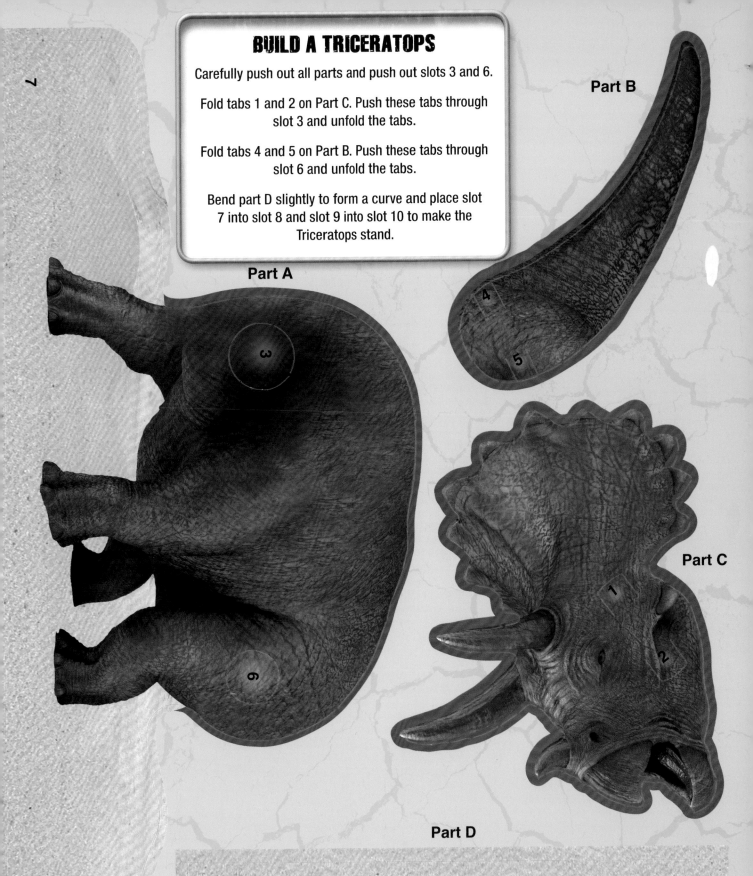

BUILD A TRICERATOPS

Carefully push out all parts and push out slots 3 and 6.

Fold tabs 1 and 2 on Part C. Push these tabs through slot 3 and unfold the tabs.

Fold tabs 4 and 5 on Part B. Push these tabs through slot 6 and unfold the tabs.

Bend part D slightly to form a curve and place slot 7 into slot 8 and slot 9 into slot 10 to make the Triceratops stand.

Part A

Part B

Part C

Part D

7

8

9

10

Giant Jigsaw

The Argentinosaurus was the largest dinosaur that has ever lived. Use your best pens to copy this picture between the grids and decorate it.

Armoured Dinosaurs

This bunch of dangerous dinosaurs were characterised by their incredible defences. Different species had different types of armour, which ranged from large, bony back plates and heavy, club-shaped tails, to bony spikes and thick, solid skin. The most well-known members of this group are Stegosaurus and Ankylosaurus.

Fact

The back legs of a Kentrosaurus were twice as big as its front legs, meaning it could walk on just its back legs for short periods of time.

Start

Stomping Ankylosaurus

Draw a line through the grid, without going diagonally or in the same square twice, so the Ankylosaurus can stomp in every empty square.

Fact

The Ankylosaurus had a clubbed tail which was powerful enough to break bones!

Prehistoric Pens

Nobody can be sure how a dinosaur's skin looked. What do you think this Euoplocephalus looked like? Use your pens to decorate this picture.

Fact

The Euoplocephalus had so much protection that it even had armoured eyelids.

10

Answers on page 18

Stegosaurus Squares

The stegosaurus is the most famous of all the armoured dinosaurs. Match each of the jigsaw pieces to a gap in this Stegosaurus picture. Which one doesn't fit?

Tyrannosaurus Chase

The Tyrannosaurus rex is having a race to prove he is the king of the dinosaurs. Play along with your friends to find out which of the dinosaurs will win the race.

How To Play

Find the dinosaur stickers on your sticker sheet and place each one on a coin to use as counters.

Each player takes a turn to roll the dice and move the counter the number rolled.

If a player lands on a special instruction square, they must follow the directions.

The winner is the first person to reach the end of the jungle path.

You Will Need

- 2-4 players
- a dice
- coins for counters
- stickers from your sticker sheet

Start

1

2

3

4
You have to avoid trampling on a nest of dinosaur eggs. Miss a go.

5

6

7
You jump across a deep gorge. Move ahead 2 spaces.

8

9

10

11
You have to find a route around a lagoon. Move back 2 spaces.

12

13

14

15

16

17
You find a shortcut through the trees. Roll the dice again.

21
Avoid getting stuck in the tar pit. Move back 2 spaces.

20

19

18

22

23

27

28

24

25

26
The Centrosaur defends its territory. Miss a go.

29

30 Finish

True or False?

Study these incredible dinosaur facts and decide whether they're amazingly true or fantastically false.

b
The two most complete Allosaurus skeletons are called Big Al and Big Al Two.

Answer.........

a
Modern-day birds are relatives of the theropod family of dinosaurs.

Answer.........

e
Tyrannosaurus rex was a ferocious hunter, but could also swim at speeds of 32 kph (20 mph).

Answer.........

c
A relative of the scorpion existed in prehistoric times. It lived in the sea and measured over 5 metres!

Answer.........

d
Pterosaurs, like modern-day birds, walked on two legs.

Answer.........

f
Stegosaurus was the only dinosaur to have a diet that consisted completely of seafood.

Answer.........

g
Herds of Velociraptor would stand on each other's shoulders to intimidate large predators.

Answer.........

h
The largest members of the sauropod family weighed as much as 12 African elephants.

Answer.........

Answers on page 16

Incredible Dinosaur Facts

Discover all kinds of amazing dinosaur facts on this page. From the longest and the heaviest, to the oldest and the most stupid, it's all covered here!

The largest flying dinosaur was the Hatzegopteryx. It stood at five metres tall and had a wingspan of at least ten metres! That's bigger than a small plane!

The Stegosaurus has the worst body-to-brain ratio of any dinosaur. It weighed two tons, but had a brain the size of a walnut, which meant it would have been very dumb.

Elasmosaurus had the longest neck of any marine reptile. The average Elasmosaurus neck was 40 metres (130 ft) long.

Larger animals have slower heartbeats, so the giant sauropods had the slowest heartbeat of all. The heart pumped blood only 5 times a minute, compared to a human's heartbeat of 72 beats a minute.

The oldest fossil ever found belonged to an Eoraptor, which lived around 228 million years ago.

The longest horned dinosaur is the Titanoceratops, which was 9 metres (30 ft) long.

Megalodon was the biggest prehistoric marine creature, measuring around 21 metres (70 ft) in length.

The largest meat-eating land dinosaur was Spinosaurus, which reached lengths of up to 17 metres (56 ft).

The first fossil discovered was that of the Mosasaurus. It was discovered in a Dutch mine in the late 1700s.

The largest dinosaur egg ever found was 30 cm (1 ft) in length and belonged to the Hypselosaurus.

Answers

Page 2 - Scary Shadows
a-4, b-5, c-1, d-2, e-3

Page 2 - Carnivore Close-ups
a-3, b-4, c-5, d-1, e-2

Page 3 - Tyrannosaurus Trails

Page 4 - Tri Again
The odd one out is marine reptile b.

Page 4 - Hiding Dinosaurs
a-6, b-3, c-4

Page 5 - Prehistoric Patterns

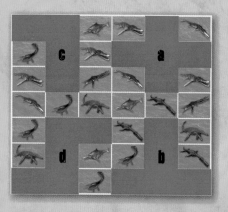

Page 6 - Loop-the-Loop
a-2, b-3, c-1

Page 6 - Matching Hatchlings
a-3, b-5, c-4, d-1, e-2

Page 8 - Fossil Hunter
The correct fossil is fossil c.

Page 8 - Cretaceous Clues
a - Auchisaurus
b - Apatosaurus
c - Titanosaurus
d - Saltasaurus

Page 10 - Stomping Ankylosaurus

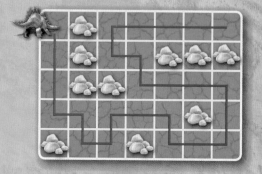

Page 11 - Stegosaurus Squares
a-3, b-5, c-4, e-2, f-1
The odd one out is d.

Page 14 - True or False?
a-true, b-true, c-true, d-false,
e-false, f-false, g-false, h-true